UNIT 17
Infinite Windows

INTER·ACTIVE

Mathematics

Activities & Investigations

GLENCOE

McGraw-Hill

New York, New York   Columbus, Ohio   Mission Hills, California   Peoria, Illinois

Send all inquiries to:
Glencoe/McGraw-Hill
936 Eastwind Drive
Westerville, OH 43081

ISBN: 0-02-824519-9 (Student Resource Book)
ISBN: 0-02-824501-6 (Teacher's Edition)

3 4 5 6 7 8 9 10 VH/LP 01 00 99 98 97 96

CONTENTS

UNIT 17
INFINITE WINDOWS
FRACTALS AND CHAOS THEORY

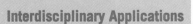

DAVID FOSTER

"The national goal is to develop mathematical power for all students. My vision for learning mathematics includes a student-oriented classroom culture, where students are taking charge of their own learning and are actively engaged in a curriculum that reflects today's world, not the mathematics of 150 years ago."

**Former Teaching Consultant
Middle Grades Mathematics
Renaissance
Morgan Hill, California**
Author of Units 1, 2, 5, 6, 7, 8, 10, 11, 13, 15,16, 17, and 18

David Foster received his B.A. in mathematics from San Diego State University and has taken graduate courses in computer science at San Jose State University. He has taught mathematics and computer science for nineteen years at the middle school, high school, and college level. Mr. Foster is a founding member of the California Mathematics Project Advisory Committee and was Co-Director of the Santa Clara Valley Mathematics Project. Most recently, he has taken the position of Consulting Author for Glencoe Publishing. Mr. Foster is a member of many professional organizations including the National Council of Teachers of Mathematics and regularly conducts in-service workshops for teachers. He is also the author of a book on computer science.

SANDIE GILLIAM

"Many students only see mathematics as isolated number facts and formulas to memorize. By using this program, which incorporates the mathematics into a context of large, real-life units tied together with literature, science, and history, the middle school student can find meaning in the mathematics."

**Mathematics Teacher
San Lorenzo Valley High School
Felton, California**
Co-author of Unit 14

Sandie Gilliam received her B.A. from San Jose State University and is a mentor teacher and instructor for the Monterey Bay Area Mathematics Project. She was a semi-finalist for the Presidential Award for Excellence in the Teaching of Mathematics in the state of California. Ms. Gilliam has served as a consultant for the California Department of Education and many local school districts and county offices of education. She is a member of the National Council of Teachers of Mathematics and is a frequent speaker at conferences and teacher in-service workshops. Ms. Gilliam was a writer and consultant for Glencoe's *Investigating Mathematics: An Interactive Approach.*

JACK PRICE

"This program is designed to help students become mathematically powerful as they develop problem-solving skills and self-reliance, as well as the ability to work well with others. At the same time, they will strengthen their basic skills and be exposed to new and exciting ideas in mathematics."

**Co-Director, Center for Science
and Mathematics Education
California State Polytechnic
University
Pomona, California**
Author of Unit 3

Jack Price received his B.A. from Eastern Michigan University and his Doctorate in Mathematics Education from Wayne State University. Dr. Price has been active in mathematics education for over 40 years, 38 of those years at grades K through 12. In his current position, he teaches mathematics and methods courses for preservice teachers and consults with school districts on curriculum change. He is president of the National Council of Teachers of Mathematics, is a frequent speaker at professional conferences, conducts many teacher in-service workshops, and is an author of numerous mathematics instructional materials.

KAY McCLAIN

"Building conceptual understanding in mathematics challenges us to re-define what it means to know and do mathematics. This program was developed to allow teachers to become facilitators of learning while students explore and investigate mathematics — strengthening their understanding and stimulating interest."

Kay McClain

Doctoral Candidate
George Peabody College
Vanderbilt University
Nashville, Tennessee
Author of Unit 9, Co-author of Unit 14

Kay McClain received her B.A. from Auburn University and her Educational Specialist degree from the University of Montevallo in Montevallo, Alabama. While a teacher at Mountain Brook Middle School in Birmingham, she received the Presidential Award for Excellence in the Teaching of Mathematics in the state of Alabama. Ms. McClain is a Woodrow Wilson fellow and a member of the National Council of Teachers of Mathematics. She regularly conducts teacher in-service workshops and is a frequent speaker at local, state, and national mathematics education conferences. She is also an author of middle school mathematics instructional materials.

BARNEY MARTINEZ

"Students learn mathematics best when their teacher enables them to become actively involved in worthwhile mathematical investigations. Students should be encouraged to interact with each other. Then, through their collaborative efforts, students build their own understanding of mathematics."

Barney Martinez

Mathematics Teacher
Jefferson High School
Daly City, California
Co-Author of Unit 12

Barney Martinez received his B.S. in mathematics from The University of San Francisco and is an instructor of pre-service mathematics teachers at the College of Notre Dame in Belmont, California. Mr. Martinez currently serves on the Mathematics Development Team of the California Department of Education and the Pursuing Excellence Revision Advisory Committee. He is a member of the National Council of Teachers of Mathematics and is very active as a speaker and workshop leader at professional development conferences.

LINDA DRITSAS

"This program is designed to encourage students to be creative and inventive, while gaining mathematical power. Open-ended situations and investigations provide the setting that allows students to work at varying depths, while nurturing their natural curiosity to learn."

Linda Dritsas

Mathematics Coordinator
Fresno Unified School District
Fresno, California
Author of Unit 4, Co-author of Unit 12

Linda Dritsas received her B.A. and M.A. from California State University at Fresno. She taught middle school mathematics for many years and, for two years, taught mathematics at California State University at Fresno. Ms. Dritsas has been the Central Section President of the California Mathematics Council and is a member of the National Council of Teachers of Mathematics and the Association for Supervision and Curriculum Development. She frequently conducts mathematics teacher in-service workshops and is an author of numerous mathematics instructional materials, including those for middle school students and teachers.

CONTRIBUTORS INTERACTIVE MATHEMATICS

Each of the Consultants read all 18 units while each Reviewer read one unit. The Consultants and Reviewers gave suggestions for improving the Student Resource Books, Teacher's Editions, Cooperative Group Cards, Posters, and Transparencies. The Writers wrote the Student Diversity Strategies that appear in the Teacher's Edition.

CONSULTANTS

Dr. Judith Jacobs, *Units 1-18*
*Director, Center for Science
and Mathematics Education
California State
Polytechnic University
Pomona, California*

Dr. Cleo M. Meek, *Units 1-18*
*Mathematics Consultant,
Retired
North Carolina Dept. of
Public Instruction
Raleigh, North Carolina*

Beatrice Moore-Harris,
*Units 1-18
College Board Equity 2000
Site Coordinator
Fort Worth Independent
School District
Fort Worth, Texas*

Deborah J. Murphy, *Units 1-18*
*Mathematics Teacher
Killingsworth Jr. High School,
ABC Unified School District
Cerritos, California*

Javier Solorzano, *Units 1-18*
*Mathematics Teacher
South El Monte High School
South El Monte, California*

WRITERS

**Student Diversity
Teacher's Edition**

Dr. Gilbert J. Cuevas
*Professor of Mathematics
Education
University of Miami
Coral Gables, Florida*

Sally C. Mayberry, *Ed.D.*
*Assistant Professor
Mathematics/Science
Education
St. Thomas University
Miami, Florida*

REVIEWERS

John W. Anson, *Unit 11*
*Mathematics Teacher
Arroyo Seco Junior High
School
Valencia, California*

Laura Beckwith, *Unit 13*
*Mathematics Department
Chairperson
William James Middle School
Fort Worth, Texas*

Betsy C. Blume, *Unit 6*
*Vice Principal/
Director of Curriculum
Valleyview Middle School
Denville, New Jersey*

James F. Bohan, *Unit 11*
*Mathematics K-12 Program
Coordinator
Manheim Township School
District
Lancaster, Pennsylvania*

Dr. Carol Fry Bohlin, *Unit 14*
*Director, San Joaquin Valley
Mathematics Project
Associate Professor,
Mathematics Education
California State University,
Fresno
Fresno, California*

David S. Bradley, *Unit 9*
*Mathematics
Teacher/Department
Chairperson
Jefferson Jr. High
Kearns, Utah*

Dr. Diane Briars, *Unit 9*
*Mathematics Specialist
Pittsburgh City Schools
Pittsburgh, Pennsylvania*

Jackie Britton, *Unit 18*
Mathematics Teacher
V. W. Miller Intermediate
Pasadena, Texas

Sybil Y. Brown, *Unit 8*
Mathematics Teacher
Franklin Alternative Middle
School
Columbus, Ohio

Blanche Smith Brownley, *Unit 18*
Supervising Director of
Mathematics (Acting)
District of Columbia Public
Schools
Washington, D.C.

Bruce A. Camblin, *Unit 7*
Mathematics Teacher
Weld School District 6
Greeley, Colorado

Cleo Campbell, *Unit 15*
Coordinator of Mathematics,
K-12
Anne Arundel County
Public Schools
Annapolis, Maryland

Savas Carabases, *Unit 13*
Mathematics Supervisor
Camden City School District
Camden City, New Jersey

W. Karla Castello, *Unit 6*
Mathematics Teacher
Yerba Buena High School
San Jose, California

Diane M. Chase, *Unit 16*
Mathematics Teacher/
Department Chairperson
Pacific Jr. High School
Vancouver, Washington

Dr. Phyllis Zweig Chinn, *Unit 9*
Professor of Mathematics
Humboldt State University
Arcata, California

Nancy W. Crowther, *Unit 17*
Mathematics Teacher
Sandy Springs Middle School
Atlanta, Georgia

Regina F. Cullen, *Unit 13*
Supervisor of Mathematics
West Essex Regional Schools
North Caldwell, New Jersey

Sara J. Danielson, *Unit 17*
Mathematics Teacher
Albany Middle School
Albany, California

Lorna Denman, *Unit 10*
Mathematics Teacher
Sunny Brae Middle School
Arcata, California

Richard F. Dube, *Unit 4*
Mathematics Supervisor
Taunton High School
Taunton, Massachusetts

Mary J. Dubsky, *Unit 1*
Mathematics Curriculum
Specialist
Baltimore City Public Schools
Baltimore, Maryland

Dr. Leo Edwards, *Unit 5*
Director, Mathematics/
Science Education Center
Fayetteville State University
Fayetteville, North Carolina

Connie Fairbanks, *Unit 7*
Mathematics Teacher
South Whittier Intermediate
School
Whittier, California

Ana Marina C. Gomezgil, *Unit 15*
District Translator/Interpreter
Sweetwater Union
High School District
Chula Vista, California

Sandy R. Guerra, *Unit 9*
Mathematics Teacher
Harry H. Rogers Middle
School
San Antonio, Texas

Rick Hall, *Unit 4*
Curriculum Coordinator
San Bernardino County
Superintendent of Schools
San Bernardino, California

Carolyn Hansen, *Unit 14*
Instructional Specialist
Williamsville Central Schools
Williamsville, New York

Jenny Hembree, *Unit 8*
Mathematics Teacher
Shelby Co. East Middle
School
Shelbyville, Kentucky

Susan Hertz, *Unit 16*
Mathematics Teacher
Paul Revere Middle School
Houston, Texas

Janet L. Hollister, *Unit 5*
Mathematics Teacher
LaCumbre Middle School
Santa Barbara, California

Dorothy Nachtigall Hren, *Unit 12*
Mathematics Teacher/
Department Chairperson
Northside Middle School
Norfolk, Virginia

Grace Hutchings, *Unit 3*
Mathematics Teacher
Parkman Middle School
Woodland Hills, California

Lyle D. Jensen, *Unit 18*
Mathematics Teacher
Albright Middle School
Villa Park, Illinois

Robert R. Jones, *Unit 7*
Chief Consultant,
 Mathematics, Retired
North Carolina Department
 of Public Instruction
Raleigh, North Carolina

Mary Kay Karl, *Unit 3*
Mathematics Coordinator
Community Consolidated
 School District 54
Schaumburg, Illinois

Janet King, *Unit 14*
Mathematics Teacher
North Gulfport Junior High
Gulfport, Mississippi

Franca Koeller, *Unit 17*
Mathematics Mentor Teacher
Arroyo Seco Junior High
 School
Valencia, California

Louis La Mastro, *Unit 2*
Mathematics/Computer
 Science Teacher
North Bergen High School
North Bergen, New Jersey

Patrick Lamberti, *Unit 6*
Supervisor of Mathematics
Toms River Schools
Toms River, New Jersey

Dr. Betty Larkin, *Unit 14*
Mathematics Coordinator
 K - 12
Lee County School District
Fort Myers, Florida

Ann Lawrence, *Unit 1*
Mathematics
 Teacher/Department
 Coordinator
Mountain Brook Jr. High
 School
Mountain Brook, Alabama

Catherine Louise Marascalco,
Unit 3
Mathematics Teacher
Southaven Elementary
 School
Southaven, Mississippi

Dr. Hannah Masterson, *Unit 10*
Mathematics Specialist
Suffolk Board of
 Cooperative Education
Dix Hills, New York

Betty Monroe Nelson, *Unit 8*
Mathematics Teacher
Blackburn Middle School
Jackson, Mississippi

Dale R. Oliver, *Unit 2*
Assistant Professor of
 Mathematics
Humboldt State University
Arcata, California

Carol A. Pudlin, *Unit 4*
Mathematics Teacher/
 Consultant
Griffiths Middle School
Downey, California

Diane Duggento Sawyer,
Unit 15
Mathematics Chairperson
Exeter Area Junior High
Exeter, New Hampshire

Donald W. Scheuer, Jr., *Unit 12*
Mathematics Department
 Chairperson
Abington Junior High
Abington, Pennsylvania

Linda S. Shippey, *Unit 8*
Mathematics Teacher
Bondy Intermediate School
Pasadena, Texas

Barbara Smith, *Unit 1*
Mathematics Supervisor,
 K-12
Unionville-Chadds Ford
 School District
Kennett Square, Pennsylvania

Stephanie Z. Smith, *Unit 14*
Project Assistant
University of Wisconsin-
 Madison
Madison, Wisconsin

Dora M. Swart, *Unit 11*
Mathematics Teacher
W. F. West High School
Chehalis, Washington

Ciro J. Tacinelli, Sr., *Unit 8*
Curriculum Director:
 Mathematics
Hamden Public Schools
Hamden, Connecticut

Kathy L. Terwelp, *Unit 12*
K-8 Mathematics Supervisor
Summit Public Schools
Summit, New Jersey

Marty Terzieff, *Unit 18*
Secondary Math Curriculum
 Chairperson
Mead Junior High School
Mead, Washington

Linda L. Walker, *Unit 18*
Mathematics Teacher
Cobb Middle School
Tallahassee, Florida

INFINITE
WINDOWS

Looking Ahead

In this unit, you will see how mathematics can be used to answer questions about chaos theory and fractal geometry. You will experience:

▶ exploring self-similarity, small numbers, and recursion

▶ creating fractals by folding and cutting paper

▶ plotting random points to create fractals

▶ using computers to investigate chaos theory and fractals

▶ creating posters with self-similar shapes

Did You Ever Wonder?

What do mathematics and learning about health careers have to do with each other? Turn the page and see how Tony Lloyd of San Antonio, Texas, combined the two!

Teens in the News

Featuring: Roger Anthony "Tony" Lloyd
Date of Birth: October 24, 1975
Date of Death: August 14, 1993
Hometown: San Antonio, Texas
Life Goal: Medical Doctor
Life Interests: Learning, writing, computers, and medicine

Tony Lloyd was about to enter his senior year of high school when he was killed in an auto accident. However, Tony accomplished a lot in his short life.

Tony attended Health Careers High School in San Antonio, Texas. His dream was to become a doctor. Teachers remember Tony as a super student, a born leader, and a talented writer. Tony's classmates described him as energetic, positive, imaginative, special, and a good dancer. Tony served as Junior Class President, and he had been elected Senior Class President. Tony volunteered for the American Heart Association and Santa Rosa Children's Hospital.

Tony valued education all of his life. He was an electronics and computer whiz and used computer-generated graphics in many of his projects. He really loved mathematics. In an autobiography of his mathematical life, he wrote, "My life in mathematics has been both eventful and fascinating. It is the only subject I take that I truly love, and hope it will be with me forever."

Tony is gone but not forgotten. He wrote many poems, short stories, and autobiographies during his life. Health Careers High School has established a scholarship fund in Tony's name. He lives on through his writing, the scholarship fund, and in the minds of all who knew him.

Ohhh!
Leave me alone!

How people want to be treated when they have a cold or flu:

Source: Sterling Health poll of 1,000 people

Left alone 77%

Don't know 7%

Waited on hand and foot 16%

Team Project

I'm Floored!

Tony had a real gift for mathematics and was highly creative. Many great architects, designers, and artists have this unusual combination of talents.

Create a ceramic tile design. Decide what size and shape your tiles will be and what colors you will use. Suppose you used your tile design to cover the floor of a lobby. Would the large design on the floor look like the design of each small, individual tile? Explain why or why not.

1953 First heart-lung machine, which makes open-heart surgery possible.

Edward Jenner develops smallpox vaccination.

1886 Aspirin first developed in Europe.

1798

1850

1980 Benoit Mandelbrot, working with fractal geometry, discovers the Mandelbrot set.

1750

2000

1950

1820 Rene Laennec invents the stethoscope.

 Alexander Fleming discovers penicillin from a mold culture.

1929

1975 Tony Lloyd born.

For more information

If you would like more information about health careers, contact:

American Medical Association (AMA)
515 North State Street
Chicago, Illinois 60610

You can learn more about the mathematics Tony used by completing the activities in this unit.

Setting the Scene

MATHEMATICS TOOLKIT

Many professions require the use of tools. This mathematics toolkit includes tools you may find useful as you study this unit. At times you may feel lost or not know where to begin when presented with a problem situation. You should take time to review this toolkit to see how the characters in the script used mathematics to solve their problem.

Narrator: Brandon, Luisa, Kou-Long, Kristi, and Poloma are members of the Students Against Drugs Club at their school. They are having a meeting to decide about the activities they are planning for their club.

Luisa: As you all know, next month is Drug Awareness Month. How are we coming with the plans for the big rally?

Kou-Long: The plans are coming along great. We have the speakers lined up and the refreshments are being ordered. Do we have an estimate for the number of people we're expecting?

Kristi: We think there'll be over 500 people there if it's advertised well. By the way, how are we going to advertise the rally?

Poloma: The national organization has sent us 200 posters to put up at school and at local businesses around town.

Luisa: That's all well and good, but what's our hook? We want to get as many kids as possible to attend. How can we really promote this?

Poloma: Well, the advertising committee has stumbled upon what we think is a great idea. When we went to Mr. Freezie's to ask if they would support us with advertising, the manager said that they would give a 5% discount for a six-month period to any student who attends the Drug Awareness Rally.

Kou-Long: Well, we thought that we could issue a card—sort of like a credit card—to each student who comes to the rally. The card could have an expiration date that is six months from the date of the rally.

Kristi: We'd better make the card look official. I can just see some people trying to use counterfeit cards.

Kou-Long: We thought we'd use the national logo on the cards. It's printed on the advertising posters.

Brandon: Cool! That'll attract a lot of students. Have you talked to any other businesses?

Kou-Long: So far, we've lined up 12 businesses that will give a discount to students attending the rally.

Luisa: That is a *fantastic* idea! But how are they going to know who to give the discount to?

STUDENTS AGAINST DRUGS
DRUG AWARENESS RALLY
WEDNESDAY
NOVEMBER
3

Luisa: Good idea. Poloma and I are office aides and our advisor says that we can use the copy machine for the club's business.

Kristi: Wait a minute. That's a big poster! How are you going to copy the logo?

Poloma: We'll reduce it using the copy machine. It can reduce and enlarge. The reductions can be 57% or 75% and it'll enlarge to 120%.

Brandon: That's going to take a lot of reducing. Can you really use the copier to make it the right size?

Poloma: Well, let's start by measuring the logo on the poster.

Kou-Long: The logo is rectangular and it measures...let me see...$10\frac{1}{2}$ inches by 8 inches.

Kristi: So, how big is a credit card?

Luisa: You know that printing business down the street, We Print It All? Well, they've donated 600 blank business cards. They're 3 inches by $2\frac{1}{4}$ inches.

Brandon: Well, good luck figuring this out. You'd better not waste a lot of time or paper, either—you know how Mr. Johnson's always saying how expensive copying is.

Stop the Script!
Determine how to reduce the logo using the copy machine.

Narrator: The students continue working on the problem.

Luisa: Okay, so where do we start?

Kristi: Let's use a calculator and experiment.

Brandon: How in the world is that going to help? A calculator won't help us see the size of the logo!

Poloma: No, but it will help us see how the size changes when we reduce it. Let's start with the length of the logo. It's $10\frac{1}{2}$ inches now. If we multiply 10.5 by 57%, how long would it be?

Kou-Long: Why would we multiply? I thought we should divide.

Kristi: If we divide 10.5 by 57%, it'll tell us how many times 57% goes into 10.5. We want to know what 57% *of* 10.5 is, so we multiply. I get 5.985.

Kou-Long: That's too long. It's got to be 3 inches long.

Luisa: Well, there's no rule that says we can't do it again!

Poloma: You think we should multiply by 57% a second time?

Luisa: Sure, let's try it.

Kristi: Okay, 5.985 times 57% is 3.41145.

Brandon: That's still too big, but I'm getting the hang of this. How about we try it one more time?

Kristi: Here goes: 3.41145 times 57% is 1.9445265.

Kou-Long: Now it's too small! I guess we can't do it.

Luisa: Don't give up so easily. There are two other buttons we could use. Let's try reducing it three times using the 75% button.

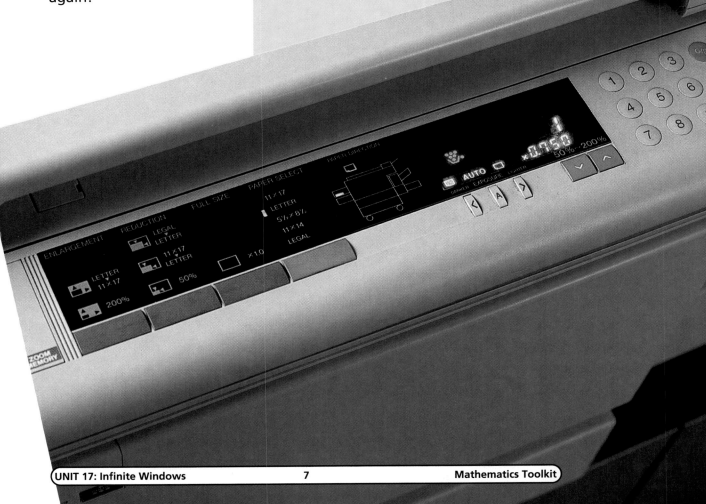

Kristi: Okay, 10.5 times 75% times 75% times 75% equals 4.4296875.

Poloma: Hey, that's way too big. It looks like we're going to have to reduce it by using both reduction buttons.

Kou-Long: Wait—maybe we're doing this backwards. I think we can find out how much we need to reduce it by setting up a ratio. Let's see:
$$\frac{reduction\ amount}{100\%} = \frac{3\ inches}{10.5\ inches}.$$
The reduction amount to the whole is the same as the new size we want to the original size.

Brandon: Okay, I'm with you. So, let's divide 3 by 10.5 to find the reduction amount.

Kristi: That's 0.2857142, or a little less than 29%.

Luisa: So, how is this going to help us?

Poloma: That's our target. We need to use 57% and 75% in some combination to get just under 29%.

Brandon: Man, this is getting complicated. Okay. We know that when we multiply 57% by itself, we get a smaller number than when we multiply 75% by itself. So, let's start from there.

Kristi: If I multiply 0.57 times 0.57, I get 0.3249.

Kou-Long: Okay, now multiply that by 75%.

Luisa: Yeah, that makes sense. Multiplying by 75% will make it even smaller.

Kristi: If I multiply 0.3249 by 0.75, I get 0.243675.

Poloma: Finally! But now I wonder if we could have gotten a little closer to the goal.

Kou-Long: I've got an idea. How about enlarging it by 120%?

Kristi: You guys, my calculator finger is killing me! Okay, 0.243675 times 1.2 equals 0.29241.

Brandon: Isn't that a little too big? Multiply the original length—10.5 inches—by 0.29241.

Kristi: You're right. The length of the logo would be 3.07 inches. That's bigger than the cards!

Poloma: I think we should stick with the reduction we got before. If we used 0.243675, how big would the logo be?

Kristi: It would be 2.56 inches long.

Poloma: Then let's put a border around the logo; that would make it look really professional. And we could put a list of the businesses that are participating on the back of the card.

Luisa: I like it! In fact, we can go print them right now. You guys can finish the meeting without us.

This concludes the Mathematics Toolkit. It included many mathematical tools for you to use throughout the unit. As you work through this unit, you should use these tools to help you solve problems. You may want to explain how to use these mathematical tools in your journal. Or you may want to create a toolkit notebook and add the mathematical tools you discover throughout this unit.

Mirror, Mirror On the Wall

Have you ever sat in a hair salon or barber shop and looked through opposite mirrors? You can look down an endless tunnel of images that are all the same. What you see is the front of your head and the back of your head in a series of identical pictures, appearing smaller and smaller, forever. Likewise, if you look at a picture of a girl holding a mirror while looking in a mirror, you experience the same thing.

Examine the picture of the girl that your teacher will show you. You and your group will write about your reactions to this picture. Be sure that you answer the following questions.

- How do the heights of the girl in the smaller pictures compare to the height of the girl in the original picture?
- If you had a microscope and could zoom in on the tenth picture of the girl, what would be the actual height of the girl in that picture?
- Suppose you could use a microscope to see something 0.0001 millimeter tall. How many pictures of the girl would you be able to see then?

Be prepared to present your group's findings to the class.

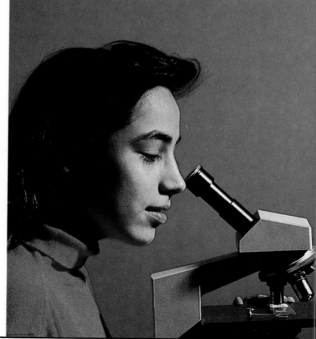

Over and Over and Over...

Folding Something into Nothing

Take an ordinary piece of paper measuring $8\frac{1}{2}$ inches by 11 inches.

1 **I**f you folded it in half with the short sides meeting, what would be the length, width, and height of the folded paper? Fold it and record your measurements.

2 **I**f you folded it in half again, this time with the long sides meeting, what would be the length, width, and height of the folded paper? Fold it again and record your measurements.

3 **C**ontinue this process, folding the paper first widthwise and then lengthwise. What would be the length, width, and height of the folded paper if you could fold it 100 times?

4 **H**ow many times would you have to fold it in order for the longest side to be less than $\frac{1}{100}$ inch long?

5 **I**magine that you could continue folding the paper forever. How many times would you have to fold it in order for the folded paper to be as tall as you are?

MENU
station
B

Double Vision

Set up two mirrors so that they are opposite each other.

1 Place a small object between the mirrors.

2 Look into the mirrors. What are the images that you see?

3 How far apart are the mirrors? How does the distance between the mirrors affect what you see?

4 Look carefully into the mirrors. How many copies of the object do you see? Sketch a drawing of what you see.

5 Estimate how much smaller the first reflection is than the original object. Estimate the size of the smallest object that you can see.

The Tortoise and the Hare

Tommy Tortoise and Harry Hare stood at the starting line of the race. Mr. Hare could run twice as fast as Mr. Tortoise. So Mr. Hare, being gracious, gave Mr. Tortoise a head start. The raceway announcer explained the running of the race in the following way. Who do you think won the race? Explain.

1 "That Harry Hare is quite a guy, isn't he folks? He's giving Mr. Tortoise quite a head start! But wait— Tommy Tortoise has just reached the halfway mark and here comes Harry Hare!"

H   T

2 "So far, folks, this race has been a real snoozer. Tommy Tortoise has just reached the three-quarter mark and as expected, Harry Hare is gaining on him. Mr. Hare has just passed the halfway point!"

H   T

3 "Harry Hare is turning on the speed, isn't he folks? He's just reached the three-quarter mark and Tommy Tortoise is now at the seven-eighths mark. It's anybody's race now!"

H T

FINISH

MENU station D

The Big Countdown

Pick a fraction between 0 and 1.

1 Use a calculator to multiply your number by itself over and over and over. You may need to convert the number to a decimal. After you enter the number, try pressing the multiplication sign and entering the number a second time. Then press the equals sign over and over. Each time you press the equals sign, the number that appears on the display is the new multiple. This method will save you time, since you won't have to enter the number every time you multiply.

2 Record your work. Keep count of the number of times that you multiply your number.

3 How fast does it take for your number to get really small?

4 When does it reach 0?

5 Try at least five different fractions. Describe what you have found and predict what would occur if you tried another number.

Follow the Bouncing Ball

A rubber ball is dropped from a 100-foot building and lands on the concrete street below.

1 **H**ow high would you estimate each bounce to be?

2 **W**hat can you predict about the behavior of the bouncing ball?

3 **W**hat might you need to know about the ball?

4 **H**ow many times do you think the ball would bounce before it comes to a complete stop? Does the ball ever really stop bouncing?

5 **H**ow high are the smallest bounces?

Conduct a number of experiments by dropping the ball from various heights. Analyze your results. Use these results and your knowledge of mathematics to draw some conclusions about a bouncing rubber ball. Write about your findings.

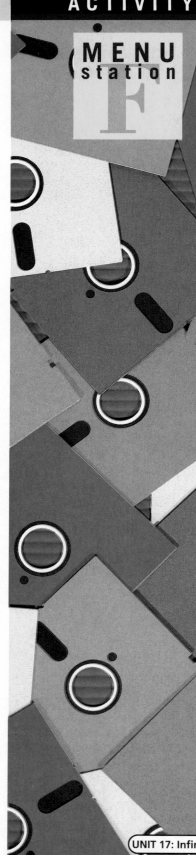

MENU station F

Squares!

Explore the following procedures that are written in LOGO on the computer.

1 **T**ype the following procedure on a computer.

To Square :x
If :x < 0.1 [Stop]
Repeat 4 [FD :x RT 90]
Square :x * 0.5
End

2 **C**arry out the procedure by typing Square 100.

3 **E**xperiment with the size of the square by changing the number that follows the word Square.

4 **A**lter the procedure by changing any of the numbers, such as 4, 90, or 0.5.

5 **E**xplain what you have discovered about the procedure.

BREAKING UP

A **fractal** is an image that has self-similarity. In this activity, create a fractal. Start with a square sheet of tissue paper 4 inches on each side.

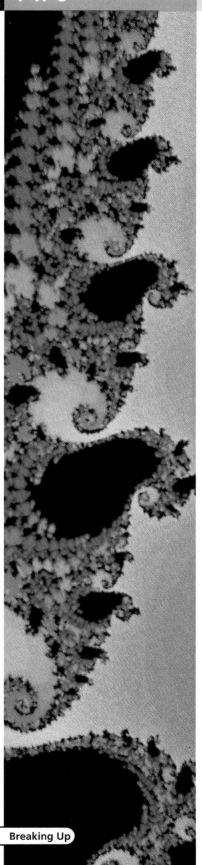

Level One

Fold the paper by bringing the right side over to the left. Then bring the top down to the bottom. If you were to open the paper up, it would be divided into 4 squares, each measuring 2 inches on a side. Now imagine cutting a square measuring $\frac{1}{2}$ inch on a side out of the upper right corner of the folded paper.

What do you think the paper will look like when it is opened up? Draw a picture to represent the paper after the square has been cut out. Then cut the square out of the upper right corner of the folded paper and open the paper up. What does it look like? How does your prediction compare to the actual result?

Level Two

Take the folded sheet and fold it again by bringing the right side over to the left and the top down to the bottom. If you were to open the paper up, it would be divided into 16 squares. Now imagine cutting another square measuring $\frac{1}{4}$ inch on a side out of the upper right corner of the folded paper. What do you think the paper will look like when it is opened up this time? Draw a picture to represent the paper after the square has been cut out. Then cut the square out of the upper right corner of the folded paper and open the paper up. What does it look like now? How does your prediction compare this time?

Level Three

Imagine that you could fold the folded sheet again so that if you were to open the paper up, it would be divided into 64

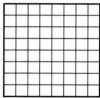

squares. Now imagine cutting an even smaller square out of the upper right corner of the folded paper. What do you think the paper will look like when it is opened up? Draw a picture to represent the paper after the square has been cut out.

Analysis

Draw a picture of the fractal created when the process is repeated to the fourth and fifth levels.

- How do each of the folded squares compare to the folded square from the previous level?
- How big was the first hole that you cut?
- How big was the second hole that you cut? Why?
- How big would the fifth hole that you cut be? Why?
- Explain what you have learned about this fractal.

Sierpinski's Triangle

Create another fractal called **Sierpinski's Triangle**. Using dot paper, choose three points to be the vertices of an equilateral triangle. Your triangle should be as large as possible. This triangle is Level Zero of this fractal.

Level Zero

Level One

Locate and mark the midpoints of each side of the triangle. Connect those three points to make a smaller, upside-down triangle in the center of the large one.

Level One

Level Two

Locate and mark the midpoints of each side of the triangle in the lower left corner. Connect those three points to make an even smaller triangle in the center of the lower left triangle. Do the same thing for the smaller triangle in the lower right corner and the triangle on the top. Leave the center triangle open.

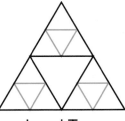

Level Two

Continue creating the fractal by repeating the process of drawing smaller triangles around each of the larger triangles. Do this for Level Three, Level Four, and so on until you cannot draw any more triangles. How many levels can you draw?

Connect the Dots

Work with a partner to complete this activity. One of you should measure and plot points. The other person will roll a number cube to determine which points to use.

Your teacher will give you a sheet of paper with three labeled points on it. Copy the points onto a blank transparency and label them. Consider the points the vertices of a triangle. Plot a fourth point anywhere on the paper to begin. We will call this point the *moving point*. Then follow the process below.

1. Roll the number cube. If you roll 1 or 4, use point 1. If you roll 2 or 5, use point 2. If you roll 3 or 6, use point 3.

2. Use a ruler to measure the distance between the moving point and the point you chose in Step 1. Plot a new point halfway between those two points. Use this point as your new moving point.

3. Continue the process by using Steps 1 and 2 over again. Plot at least 50 points.

Then describe in writing the figure that you made. Also describe what you think the figure would look like if you plotted 500 points.

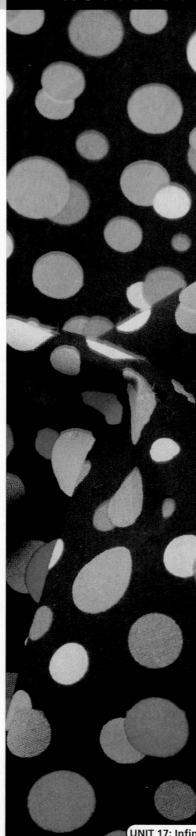

Use the technique that you followed on the previous page to create two more fractals.

Your teacher will give you a sheet of paper with four labeled points on it. Copy the points onto a blank transparency and label them. Plot a moving point anywhere on the page.

1. Roll a number octahedron (a solid with 8 numbered faces). If you roll 1 or 5, use point 1. If you roll 2 or 6, use point 2. If you roll 3 or 7, use point 3. If you roll 4 or 8, use point 4.
2. Use a ruler to measure the distance between the moving point and the point you chose in Step 1. Plot a new point $\frac{2}{3}$ of the way between the moving point and the point you chose in Step 1. Use this point as your new moving point.
3. Continue the process by using Steps 1 and 2 over again. Plot at least 100 points.

Your teacher will give you a sheet of paper with eight labeled points on it. Copy the points onto a blank transparency and label them. Plot a moving point anywhere on the page.

1. Roll a number octahedron.
2. Use a ruler to measure the distance between the moving point and the point you rolled in Step 1. Plot a new point $\frac{2}{3}$ of the way between the moving point and the point you rolled in Step 1. Use this point as your new moving point.
3. Continue the process by using Steps 1 and 2 over again. Plot at least 100 points.

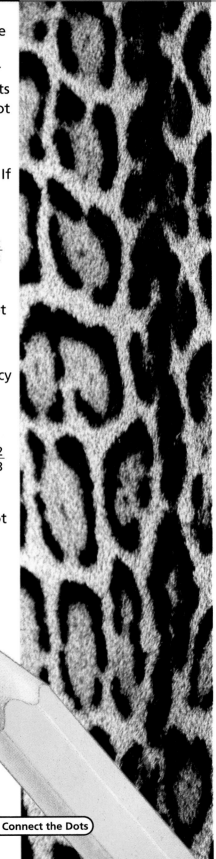

COMPUTER
investigation

It's Chaos!

In this activity, you will use a computer program called Chaos to create a fractal. Load the program by typing **LOAD "CHAOS**. To run the program, type **BEGIN**.

1. The program will prompt you as follows: **Type in the number of coordinate pairs:**. Choose a figure as the basis for your fractal. You can use a triangle, a square, a rectangle, or a hexagon. Enter the number of vertices in your figure; for example, 3 for a triangle, 4 for a square or rectangle, and so on.

2. The program will prompt you again: **Type in coordinate pair number 1:**. The screen is like a coordinate plane. 0 0 is the exact center of the screen. The first number refers to the left or right direction, and the second number refers to the up or down direction. For example, 100 100 is right 100 and up 100; –100 0 is just left 100. Enter the coordinates of

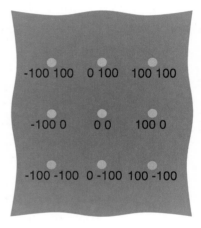

the point as two numbers separated by a space. Do *not* use commas or parentheses when entering coordinates.

3. The program will prompt you a third time: **Type in coordinate pair number 2:**. Enter the coordinates of the second point as two numbers separated by a space. The program will continue to prompt you until all of the coordinates have been entered. Here are some possible coordinates for the four figures.

triangle: (0 100), (–100 –100), (100 –100)
square: (–100 –100), (100, –100), (100 100), (–100 100)
hexagon: (40 80), (100 0), (40 –80), (–60 –80), (–120 0), (–60 40)
8-point   (–100 –100), (0 –100), (100 –100), (100 0),
rectangle: (100 100), (0 100), (–100 100), (–100 0)

COMPUTER investigation

4. Then, the program will prompt you as follows: **Type in the coordinates of the starting point:**. Experiment with this point; put it anywhere on the screen.
5. To stop the process, press Ctrl-G if you have an Apple II computer, Ctrl-Break if you have an IBM-compatible computer, or Option if you have a Macintosh computer.

Analyze your findings in a one-page report. Here are some things to consider.

• Record your results. Classify the images you created, look for patterns in the images, and sketch drawings of some of the images.

• Record the inputs that you used and determine how they affected the images you created. How did changing the location of the points affect an image?

• How many levels can you see? What is the size of the smallest subsection that you can see?

• Consider how long the program needs to run in order to obtain a clear picture of the image emerging. Be prepared to discuss your findings.

• Summarize your findings. What did you discover about chaos theory?

Forest Fire

You and your partner are forest rangers who are concerned about the spread of forest fires in your area. You know that fires spread in a random manner, so you run several chaos games to simulate the burning of the forest in order to make predictions about your area.

To run the simulation, select a probability factor for the spread of the fire. In other words, select a fraction that will predict the likelihood that the fire will spread. Choose from $\frac{1}{6}$, $\frac{2}{6}$ or $\frac{1}{3}$, $\frac{3}{6}$ or $\frac{1}{2}$, $\frac{4}{6}$ or $\frac{2}{3}$, or $\frac{5}{6}$. If you choose $\frac{1}{6}$, that means that the fire will spread only $\frac{1}{6}$ of the time. If you choose $\frac{5}{6}$, the fire will be much more likely to spread.

Each tree in the forest has four neighbors: one to the north, one to the east, one to the south, and one to the west. When a tree is on fire, any one of its neighbors that is not already burned has a chance to catch fire. Each fire lasts one hour. Roll a number cube to determine whether or not a tree catches fire. Depending on your probability factor and the number that you roll, the tree may or may not catch fire. See the table below.

To start the fire, choose a square on your grid paper and label it "1." This means that the tree is burning during the first hour. During this hour, each of its four neighbors will have a chance to catch fire. Roll the number cube to determine if the neighbor to the north will catch fire. If it does, label it "2," because it will be burning during the second hour.

Probability Factor	Catches Fire if You Roll...
$\frac{1}{6}$	1
$\frac{2}{6}$	1, 2
$\frac{3}{6}$	1, 2, 3
$\frac{4}{6}$	1, 2, 3, 4
$\frac{5}{6}$	1, 2, 3, 4, 5

If it does not catch fire, do not label the square. Next, roll the number cube to see if the neighbor to the east will catch fire. If it does, label it "2." Continue with the neighbors to the south and west. If only the neighbors to the east and south caught fire, your grid paper would look like Figure 1.

Figure 1

When all four neighbors have been checked, the first hour is over. During the second hour, each of the trees labeled "2" is on fire, and each of its neighbors that are not already burned must be checked. These neighbors are labeled "*" in Figure 2. You do not need to label the neighbors when you run your simulation.

The tree that is circled will have two chances to catch fire during the second hour, since two of its neighbors are burning. If any of the neighbors catch fire during this hour, label them "3," because they will be burning during the third hour. When all of these neighbors have been checked, the second hour is over. Only the trees labeled "3" are burning, and their neighbors must be checked during the third hour. Continue the simulation and stop when there are no more trees burning or when the fire has burned beyond the boundaries of the forest.

Figure 2

Run several simulations using different probability factors for the spreading of the fire. Try to determine which probability factors will cause the fire to burn out before reaching the boundaries of the forest, and which will cause the fire to spread unchecked. Investigate how the probability affects the shape of the burned area. For those fires that burn out, determine how many trees are consumed by the fire before it dies out.

In your role as forest ranger, write to your supervisor about the likelihood of a fire spreading in your area. Predict how the fires will burn. Discuss what damage will occur when the fire spreading factor changes and what could cause this factor to increase.

The Color Triangle
Multiples

The figure on the sheet your teacher has provided is called **Pascal's Triangle**. Describe any patterns you notice in the first five rows. Then use the pattern to continue the triangle until you have 20 rows.

Each person in your group should roll the number cube. Anyone who rolls a 1 or rolls the same number as another person in the group must roll again. When each of you has your own number, you each should select one color for the multiples of your number and another color for those numbers that are not multiples. For example, if your number is 3, you would have one color for the multiples of 3: 3, 6, 9, 12, and so on, and another for the numbers that are not multiples.

Consider each number in Pascal's Triangle. Is it a multiple of your number? Color each hexagon with the colors you selected. Once everyone in your group has colored their triangle, compare all of the triangles. As a group, make a list of the similarities and differences among your colored triangles.

Make a group poster. Glue each of your triangles, along with your list of similarities and differences, onto the poster.

Remainders

Roll the number cube again to select another number. This time, you will color the triangle based on remainders. For example, if you roll a 3 and you divide a number in the triangle by 3, the possible remainders are 0, 1, and 2. Assign a different color to each of these remainders. Then consider each number in the triangle. Divide each number by 3 and color the entry according to its remainder.

Write about the triangle that you colored. Address the following questions in your remarks.
- What does the triangle look like?
- How does it compare to the triangle that you colored before?
- What do you think would happen if you had rolled a different number?

COMPUTER investigation

Fractured Pictures

In this activity, you will use a computer program called Fractals to create a fractal. Load the program by typing **LOAD "FRACTALS**. To run the program, type **BEGIN**.

1. The program will prompt you as follows: **Type in the number of sides:**. Choose a polygon as the basis for your fractal and enter the number of sides it has. This is the first level of the fractal image.

2. The second prompt will be: **Type in the length of a side:**. Choose a number between 80 and 200. The smaller the number of sides, the larger the length of a side should be.

3. The third prompt will be: **Type in the turning angle:**. This is an angle measurement between 0° and 360°. Divide 360 by the number of sides and enter the result.

4. The fourth prompt will be: **Type in the fractal divisor:**. This number adjusts the size of the subparts of the fractal. For example, 2 will make each part one-half the size of the original, 3 will make each part one-third the size of the original, and so on.

5. The fifth prompt will be: **Type in the number of copies:**. This refers to the number of copies that are made from the original figure. This number should be the same as the number of sides.

6. The sixth prompt will be: **Type in the depth of the fractal:**. This is the number of sublevels that will be drawn. The higher the number, the more dense the fractal. Try numbers between 3 and 6.

7. Finally, **Type in the location of the lower left corner of your figure:**. This location is the point from which the fractal is drawn. The location can be anywhere on the screen.

Look for patterns in the images and sketch drawings of some of the images. Then write a report describing all of the properties of fractals that you have discovered in this unit. Be prepared to share your findings with the class.

Go Fly a Kite

Step 1

In this activity, you will build two kites, each in the shape of a **tetrahedron**. A tetrahedron is a pyramid in which each of the four sides, or *faces*, is in the shape of a triangle. Thus, there are three triangles at each vertex.

Make each tetrahedron kite with six straws that are the same length. Join the straws together using twist ties and/or tape at four points. Cover two of the faces with tissue paper by wrapping the paper around two of the four faces and securely taping the paper around the straws. Place the kite so that one of the open sides is on the bottom and the other is facing you.

Step 2

Pair up with another student in your class. Use your four tetrahedra to build a large tetrahedron. Place three of the tetrahedra together to form a base and place the fourth tetrahedron on top. Tape the four smaller kites together at the points where they meet. Make sure that the small kites are aligned so that the tissue paper covers two of the larger faces.

Step 3

Join three other pairs of students in your class. At this point, there should be eight of you and four large tetrahedra. Use these four tetrahedra to build an even larger tetrahedron. Place three of the large tetrahedra together to form a base and place the fourth large tetrahedron on top. Tape the four tetrahedra together at the points where they meet. Once again, make sure that the kites are aligned so that the tissue paper covers two of the large faces.

YOUR REPORT

Write about your kites.

- Analyze the components of your group kite. Describe the self-similar shapes that appear in it.

- Describe the size relationship of the shapes between the levels of the group kite.

- Predict the sizes of the components of the kite if it were to grow larger. For example, what size would the kite be if it were built to level 10?

- Suppose the kite was made up of an infinite number of sublevels; that is, the kite was made of infinitely many smaller kites. What method could you use to find the length of a side of the kite at any level?

I've Got Designs on You

Design a poster that contains a fractal, a self-similar collage, a picture inside a picture, a self-similar geometric design, or another self-similar original creation. It must be an original drawing or design. Your poster may contain photographs, pictures from periodicals, enlargements or reductions from copiers, and/or computer-generated designs. The object can be created by using a chaos technique or a self-similar drawing. You may produce a 3-dimensional model of a fractal. Your design must contain at least four levels of self-similar shapes.

This is an enlargement of the photo of a fractal shown at the right.

YOUR REPORT

Write an individual report that describes the poster and the process that you used to create the design. Be sure to describe the relationship between similar objects in your design. Identify the self-similar shapes or pictures that you used in the poster. Determine the relationship between the sizes of self-similar shapes that you used. Determine a procedure for finding the size of that shape at any given level of the design. Then prepare an oral presentation that includes your poster and written report.

Selection and Reflection

- The mathematical terms **self-similarity, chaos, fractal geometry, infinity,** and **recursion** were used throughout this unit. What do these terms mean? Explain them in your own words and give examples.

- What do these words mean in terms of the work you did in this unit?

- Describe the mathematics that you used in this unit.

- What did you learn while studying this unit? Use examples from several of the activities in the unit in your explanation.

- How did you feel about learning about fractals and chaos theory? Did you enjoy the experience?

The Problem

When books are printed, large sheets of paper are run through the printing presses. These sheets are then folded in half twice to form the pages of the book. Imagine that you are a bookbinder. Take two sheets of paper each measuring $8\frac{1}{2}$ inches by 11 inches. Fold and number the pages in your booklet from 1 to 8. How many sheets of paper would be needed to make a 120-page booklet? What rule or rules can be used to assign numbers to each sheet of paper?

Book Him

The Best Deal

The Problem

Your parents have offered you a choice in the way that you can receive your allowance. You can get $50.00 per month, or you can get 1¢ the first day, 2¢ the second day, 4¢ the third day, 8¢ the fourth day, and so on, doubling the amount each day. Which deal would you agree to? Why?

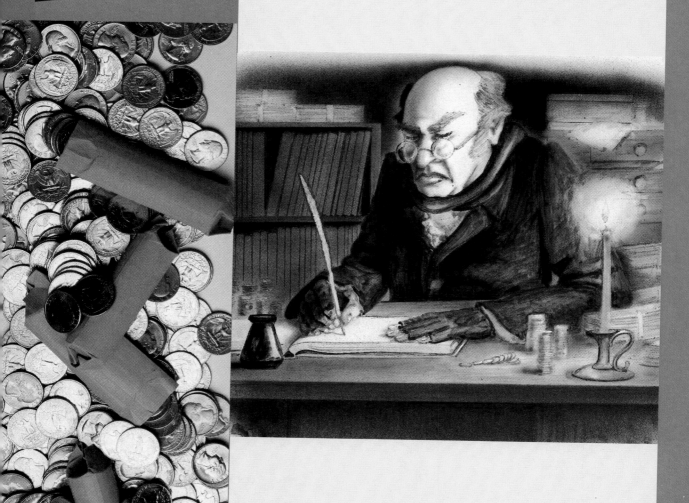

The Problem

At 8:00 A.M., you told your best friend a deep, dark secret. Then, within 15 minutes, your best friend told two other people. Then, within the next 15 minutes, those two people each told two other people. This continued all day long, with every person telling two other people who hadn't been told every 15 minutes. How many people would know your deep, dark secret by 3:00 P.M.? Write a letter to your best friend explaining what happened to your secret.

The Deep, Dark Secret

The Staircase

The Problem

A certain staircase has 10 steps. Esteban is able to climb up the staircase by either going up the steps one at a time or by going up two steps at a time. How many different ways can he climb the staircase? Keep in mind that taking a single step, then a double step, and then 7 more single steps is a different way to go up the staircase than first taking a double step and then 8 single steps.

Extension In how many ways could Esteban go up and down the stairs if he could take single or double steps each way?

The Problem

Suppose the copier at your school can reduce pictures to 57% and 64% and can enlarge pictures to 120%. You have a picture that you need to reduce to exactly 25% of the original. Determine a method for reducing the original to get the picture as close to 25% of the original as possible.

PASCAL'S TRIANGLE

The Problem

The triangular array of numbers shown at the right is called Pascal's Triangle, for the French mathematician Blaise Pascal. The triangle was published in Europe in 1665, but a Chinese version of the triangle was published in 1303.

```
            1
          1   1
        1   2   1
      1   3   3   1
    1   4   6   4   1
```

Find the sum of the numbers in each row of the triangle. How is the sum of a row related to the sum of the row just above it?

Extension How is the sum of the numbers in any row of Pascal's Triangle related to the sum of the numbers in all of the rows above the given row?

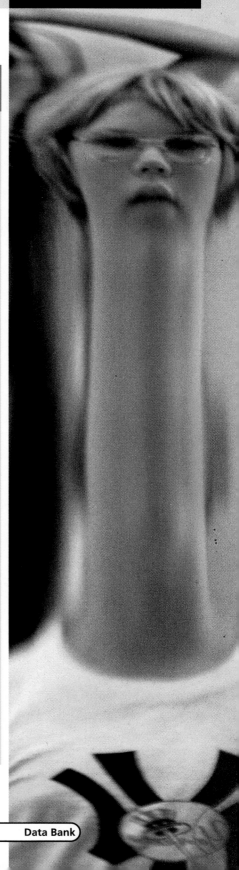

TABLE OF CONTENTS

You can buy a signal mirror for a buck or so at any backcountry or army/navy surplus store. A signal mirror is lightweight and unbreakable, and tucks easily into a pack or pocket. One will also do double duty as a grooming mirror in camp. As a signaling device, it can be life-saving if used properly, sending out a flash visible for up to 10 miles in clear weather.

A survival mirror is glossy on both sides and has a hole drilled near the center. The hole is used as a sight for directing a flash-signal to a precise target. Here's how it works. Sight your target through the center hole, holding the mirror a few inches from your face. Depending on the angle of the sun, this will cause a spot of sunlight to fall either on your face or on your free hand, which should be raised parallel to the mirror. (If the dot lights on your face, you'll see the reflection in the mirror.) Next, tilt the mirror slowly while sighting your target object. When the sun dot aligns with the center hole in the mirror, your flash signal is landing on target.

Send flashes in groups of three: three quick flashes, three slower ones, three more quick ones, which is the standard Morse code SOS call.

Source: Anthony Acerrano, "Signaling for Help," *Sports Afield*, January 1991

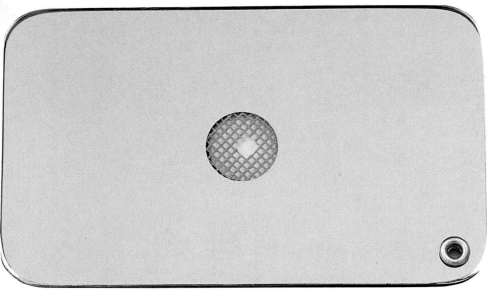

The latter part of the Sung Dynasty, 960–1280 A.D., through the early part of the Yüan Dynasty, 1280–1368 A.D., was the greatest time in ancient Chinese mathematics. Among the many notable Chinese mathematicians of this time were Yang Hui and Chu Shï-kié. The earliest known presentation of Pascal's Triangle was given by Yang Hui. Chu Shï-kié spoke of the triangle as being ancient in his time in a book written in 1303.

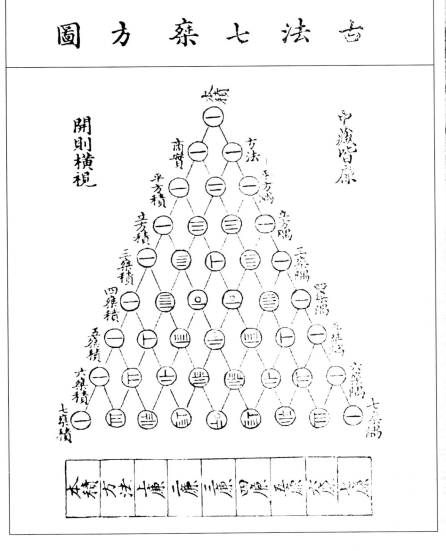

LOGO Command	Description
DRAW	A clear screen appears with the turtle located in the center of the screen.
FD	Move forward. It is followed by the number of units to m.
BK	Move back. It is followed by the number of units to moe.
RT	Turn right (clockwise). It is followed by the number of degrees to turn.
LT	Turn left (counterclockwise). It is followed by the number of degrees to turn.
PU	Pen-Up allows you to move the turtle without drawing.
PD	Pen-Down resumes drawing at that point.
REPEAT	Used with a number and brackets as in REPEAT X[ ]. Repeats the commands inside the brackets X number of times. You must replace X with a number.

The HOME Screen

The turtle is located in the center of the screen. The screen is 278 units from left to right and 238 units from top to bottom.

The HOME screen appears whenever you use DRAW.

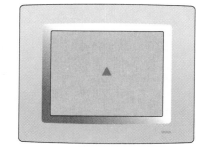

Programs

To create a program, type TO and the name you wish to give the program. Press the RETURN key.

A screen appears with your program name at the top. Enter the commands you wish the program to contain. Follow the directions at the bottom of the screen to get back to the DRAW screen.

To run the program, type the name and press the RETURN key.

How Firefighters Battle Wildfires

Firefighters used a three-pronged approach to battling the California wildfires in 1993. Protection of life and property was the first priority.

ENGINES

Engine companies, assigned to streets and homes, protect houses by wetting down brush, hillsides and sometimes roofs. They fight blazes in buildings that catch fire.

HAND CREWS

Teams of 15-16 people use shovels, chain saws and other tools to clear brush and trees, making a clear fire line about 3-6 feet wide. Strong winds usually make it too dangerous to work at the front of the fire. Bulldozers cut wider paths, but can't work on hillsides.

AIRCRAFT

Helicopters drop up to 360 gallons of water at a time directly on the flames. Tanks can be refilled in a minute. Airplane tankers drop a fire-retardant material ahead of the flames. Aircraft will sometimes be used to protect a threatened house.

FIRESTORMS

Whirling masses of hot air called firestorms can wreak havoc:

1 Hot air from fire rises, pulling in fresh air from ground level.

2 Winds cause a pillar of hot air to whirl, adding to speed of movement.

3 The faster the fire burns, the hotter it burns, the faster air is pulled into the fire.

4 Rising winds can suck up embers and spread them over thousands of feet.

PROTECTION

Crews are dressed in Nomex, a fire-resistant material, and carry pup-tent like shelters, known as "shake and bakes," for protection if flames are about to overrun them.

FLAMES

Fire usually burns uphill, but can spread whichever way the wind blows, and can jump 8-lane highways.

Winds Fuel Fires

Hot, dry "Santa Ana winds" fueled fires in California. Where they come from:

1 Air pushed from a high-pressure area over Colorado speeds toward low-pressure area over California.

3 Air pushes through mountains, gaining speed.

4 At coast, winds channeled through canyons can reach 90 mph or more with just 5%-10% humidity.

2 Air loses moisture as it moves up mountains.

Nevada Utah Colorado Calif. Arizona

Source: Los Angeles County Fire Department; *USA Today* Research, Weather Services Corp.

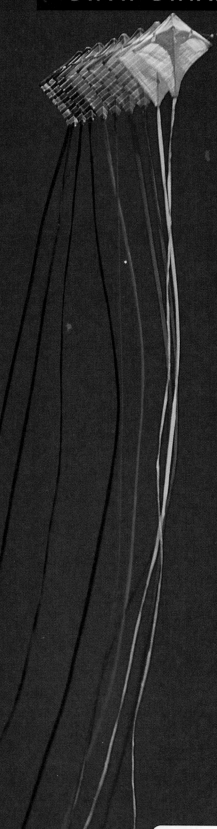

A universal symbol in art, literature, and folklore, the kite is an efficient and peaceful aircraft. The earliest historic references date to the fourth century B.C., when Kungshu Phan, a Chinese engineer, reportedly sent aloft a "wooden bird." Accounts of kites are also found in the annals of ancient Egypt and Greece.

From Benjamin Franklin's experiments with electricity to the Wright Brothers' first flight, kites have played key roles in scientific discovery and the study of weather. But even for scientists, kite flying can represent a way to relax and have fun. Alexander Graham Bell, the inventor of the telephone, designed a massive six-sided kite that could carry a person into the air.

In the modern world, the venerable kite is experiencing a renaissance that may carry with it a new role as a symbol of global cooperation. The historic 1985 summit meeting of Presidents Ronald Reagan of the United States and Mikhail Gorbachev of the USSR marked a significant step towards peace between the super-powers. The spirit of that meeting inspired American kite designer Jane Parker-Ambrose to create a kite commemorating this new promise of global harmony. The flags of the US and the USSR are joined on the face of the kite. Halley's Comet, which revisited Earth in 1986 for the first time in seventy-six years, is shown as a portent of peace.

On a "people to people" visit to Moscow that year, Jane presented her kite, along with a letter of friendship signed by some 300 kite flyers from the US, Canada, Japan, and the United Kingdom, to the Soviet Women's Peace Committee. This gesture of international goodwill gave birth to the idea for One Sky, One World, an annual global kite-fly held each year on the second Sunday in October. A non-profit organization based in Denver, Colorado, its mission is to focus the entire planet's attention on the need to maintain peace and protect the environment. (For information about how to take part, write to: One Sky, One World, P.O. Box 11149, Denver, CO 80211, USA.)

The first One Sky, One World kite-fly took place in 1986, with more than 10,000 kites and 40,000 participants at ninety locations in fourteen countries. In just six years, the event has grown to include more than 250,000 people in twenty-four countries. In October 1991, One Sky, One World events were held in Moscow, Washington, DC, Bombay, Berlin, Sydney, Beijing, and many other major cities. Kite-flyers from Japan, France, Colombia, Guam, Chile, England, Hungary, Italy, The Netherlands, Scotland, Spain, Hawaii, Alaska, and many other US locations joined in.

Source: Tom Krol, "One Sky, One World," *UNESCO Courier*, July-August 1992

COVER: Gregory Sams/Science Photo Library/Photo Researchers;

iii, 1(l), Courtesy Lupe Lloyd, (r), **2**(l), K S Studios/Bob Mullenix, (t), Courtesy Lupe Lloyd; **3**(t), BLT Productions/Brent Turner, (r), (screened), K S Studios/Bob Mullenix, (cl), The Bettmann Archive, (cr), Aaron Haupt Photography, (bl), Steve Niedorf/The Image Bank, (bc), Doug Martin, (br), Courtesy Lupe Lloyd; **4, 5,**(t)(b), BLT Productions/Brent Turner, (c), Studiohio; **6, 7**(t), BLT Productions/Brent Turner, (b), K S Studios/Bob Mullenix; **8,** Todd Yarrington; **9,** BLT Productions/Brent Turner; **10**(l), K S Studios/Bob Mullenix, (r), Matt Meadows; **11**(l), Felicia Martinez/ PhotoEdit, (r), Studiohio; **12**(l), Janice Sheldon/Photo 20-20, (r), Scott Cunningham; **13**(t), Gene Frazier, (b), William J. Weber; **14,** Jeffrey Sylvester/FPG; **15,** Studiohio; **16,** W. Cody/WestLight; **17,** Homer W. Smith/Peter Arnold, Inc; **18,** Scott Camazine/Photo Researchers/ **19,** Gregory Sams/Science Photo Library/Photo Researchers; **20,** Studiohio; **21,** Steve Bentsen/Stock Imagery; **22,** Hickson-Bender Photography; **23**(l), Gregory Sams/Science Photo Library/Photo Researchers, (r), Hickson-Bender Photography; **24,** Stan Osolinski/The Stock Market; **25,** David Frazier Photo Library/PhotoBank; **26**(l), Studiohio, (b), Ken Ross/FPG; **27**(l), Masa Uemura/AllStock, (r) Chuck O'Rear/WestLight; **28,** Gregory Sams/Science Photo Library/Photo Researchers; **29,** Gene Stein/WestLight; **30,** Ron Rovtar; **31,** Carlos Ginzburg; **33,** Alvis Upitus/The Image Bank; 34, K S Studios/Bob Mullenix; **35,** Scott Cunningham; **36,** Doug Martin; **38,** The Bettmann Archive; **39,** Judith Arson/Peter Arnold, Inc; **40,** Scott Cunningham; **41,** Grant V. Faint/The Image Bank; **42,** Tim Courlas; **44,** Aaron Haupt Photography; **45**(l), Axel Voss/One Sky One World.

ACKNOWLEDGMENTS

40, Reprinted from *Sports Afield* magazine, January 1991 Issue. Copyright 1991 The Hearst Corporation. All Rights Reserved.; **41,** Joseph Needham, *Science and Civilisation in China,* Volume III, Cambridge: Cambridge University Press, 1959, p. 135. **44-45,** Tom Krol, "One Sky, One World," *UNESCO Courier*, July-August 1992. Reprinted from the UNESCO Courier.